Look and Find®

DISNEY PRINCESS

ROYAL WEDDING

pi kids® publications international, ltd.

Cinderella's dream comes true when her prince asks her to marry him! Can you find these royal rings hiding around the palace garden?

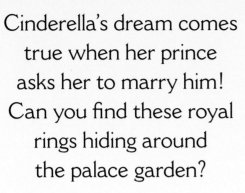

Cinderella must learn to be a princess, just like the brides who served the kingdom long ago. Can you find these portraits of princesses past?

Cinderella wants to combine royal traditions with her own family's traditions to make her wedding truly special! Can you help Cinderella find these things to help plan her wedding?

Cinderella's wedding day has arrived! She watches from her window as the entire kingdom celebrates. Search the crowd for these festive people that she sees.

Bridal Shoppe

Keepsakes

MEMORIES

CELEBRATION FLOWERS

GLASS SLIPPERS

The palace kitchen is filled
with wonderful treats for
Cinderella's wedding guests.
Can you find these things
that Cinderella requested?

It's almost time for
the royal wedding!
Look for these things
that Cinderella might
want before she walks
down the aisle.

The bride and groom are showered with beautiful flower petals as they walk down the aisle. Can you find these flowers Cinderella's friends put together for her royal wedding?

Cinderella's friends are so happy that her dreams have come true! Everyone wants to celebrate. Can you find Cinderella's friends at her royal banquet?

Go back to the palace garden to find these lovebirds around Cinderella and her prince.

Return to the portrait room to find these things that belonged to princesses long ago.

Cinderella has a lot to learn about being a princess! Return to Cinderella's room to find these books on everything royal.

Royal Traditions

Royal HISTORY

Royal Lineage

Royal Customs

ROYAL WARDROBE

Royal Manners

Can you find these royal wedding souvenirs in the crowd by the palace?

CHARMING

CHARMING CINDERELLA

CINDERELLA

Go back to the kitchen to look for serving pieces fit for a new princess.

Return to Cinderella's room and look for these wedding gifts.

Return to Cinderella's wedding ceremony to look for guests wearing these fancy hats.

Love is in the air at Cinderella's wedding. Can you find these lovestruck souls at the royal banquet?